HERO

Castle
Mission

Steve Barlow and Steve Skidmore
Illustrated by David Lang

I HERO

Code
Mission

Steve Barlow and Steve Skidmore
Illustrated by Sonia Leong

LONDON·SYDNEY

First published in 2007
by Franklin Watts

Text © Steve Barlow and Steve Skidmore 2007
Illustrations © Sonia Leong 2007
Cover design by Jonathan Hair

Franklin Watts
338 Euston Road
London NW1 3BH

Franklin Watts Australia
Level 17/207 Kent Street
Sydney, NSW 2000

A CIP catalogue record for this book
is available from the British Library.

ISBN: 978 0 7496 7667 4

3 5 7 9 10 8 6 4

Printed in Great Britain

Franklin Watts is a division of Hachette Children's Books,
an Hachette Livre UK company.

Decide your own destiny...

This book is not like others you may have read. *You* are the hero of this adventure. It is up to you to make decisions that will affect how the adventure unfolds.

Each section of this book is numbered. At the end of most sections, you will have to make a choice. The choice you make will take you to a different section of the book.

Some of your choices will help you to complete the adventure successfully. But choose carefully, some of your decisions could be fatal!

If you fail, then start the adventure again and learn from your mistake.

If you choose correctly you will succeed in your adventure.

Don't be a zero, be a hero!

It is May 1944. You are an agent of the British Special Intelligence Service (SIS) – a top-secret unit. You speak several languages and are an expert in handling many types of weapon. During the course of the war against Nazi Germany, you have taken part in many successful operations behind enemy lines.

The war is now coming to a crucial turning point. *Operation Overlord*, the codename for the Allied invasion of mainland Europe, is scheduled to take place in a month's time.

During the last six months, you have carried out several spy missions in northern France in preparation for the invasion. Now, having completed your latest mission, you are back in London on leave.

However, your well-earned break is interrupted by a phone call from General Alan Cummings, the head of your section at SIS.

"Sorry to disturb you, old bean," he says. "But there's a bit of a flap going on and I need you over here at HQ. I've sent a driver. He'll be there in a jiffy." He rings off, leaving you to wonder what sort of mission you are needed for.

Now turn to section 1.

1

The car arrives and takes you across London to the secret HQ of the SIS, where you are shown into the general's office.

General Cummings is sitting at his desk, looking worried. "We have a problem that only you can help us with," he says. "We've had a report that the Nazis have captured a key member of the French Resistance in Normandy. His agent codename is Latrec."

You gasp – you have worked with Latrec behind enemy lines.

"Another report confirms that he is being held prisoner in a small village near Caen."

"I know Latrec," you say. "He won't talk."

"Unfortunately, that's not the problem. He was captured with a top-secret code-breaking machine."

You nod. "Like the stolen Enigma machine that we use to break the Nazi secret Enigma codes."

"Exactly. Latrec was using this machine to decode the orders we were sending to the French Resistance. Their help is vital if

Operation Overlord is to succeed. If the Nazis realise how important this machine is, they will be able to break our codes. They will know when and where *Operation Overlord* is going to take place, and the whole thing will go belly-up. I need you to go to France and sort this mess out. We're short of time, so you'll be going in alone. It's going to be dangerous – are you up for it?"

If you wish to ask for time to think about this request, go to 19.

If you wish to volunteer, go to 27.

2

You realise that this man is not your contact – he has given you an old codename.

"Very well," you say, "take me to Latrec." He smiles and turns his back.

Taking your opportunity, you strike him on the head with the butt of your revolver. He crashes to the floor.

"Well done. Although, I would have shot him."

Startled at this new voice, you spin round. A woman is standing there. She is pointing a gun at you. "Smith, I presume," she says. "Don't worry. I'm not going to shoot you. I am Pierre Blanc."

You nod – she is the real French Resistance contact. "And who is he?" you ask, pointing at the unconscious figure on the floor.

"This man is a traitor – he was the one who betrayed Latrec to the Gestapo, the German secret police."

"What are you going to do with him?" you ask.

"The Resistance has a way of dealing with traitors. Now, you must come with me."

Go to 33.

3

You cut yourself free from the harness and drop to the ground. You hear movement. You crouch behind a tree and see the figure of a large man approaching. He is dressed in civilian clothes and carrying a rifle.

If you wish to hide behind the trees, go to 22.
If you wish to attack the man, go to 47.
If you wish to talk to him, go to 26.

4

"The best bet is to get into the field and circle behind the half-track," you say.

Carefully, you crawl into the cornfield and make your way behind the armoured half-track.

You realise that there are only four soldiers. They all have their backs to you and you have a clear shot.

If you decide to shoot the soldiers, go to 8.
If you have another idea, go to 39.

5

"We've got to carry on!" you tell the pilot. "This mission is vital."

The next few minutes are a nightmare as shells explode around the plane. Finally you pass over the air defences.

"That was close," says the pilot. "Now let's get you to where you need to be."

Minutes later you are standing in the doorway of the plane, parachute on, guns strapped to your body, ready for the pilot's command. The air roars around you as you prepare to jump.

"Drop zone coming up!" shouts the pilot. "Five seconds…"

You count down. "5…4…3…2…1…" and launch yourself into the blackness of the night.

Go to 23.

6

As you turn to follow, the man suddenly swings his rifle butt and cracks you on the head. You fall to the ground, unconscious.

Go to 12.

7

You decide to open your chute at three hundred metres and pull at the ripcord. Your parachute opens, but you have left it too late to control your landing – you realise you are travelling too fast. You are going to hit the ground, hard!

You see the outline of a forest below you – maybe that will help to break your fall, if it doesn't break your neck first!

If you wish to try and steer towards the forest, go to 18.

If you don't wish to risk hitting the trees, go to 43.

8

The German soldiers stand no chance as you pull the trigger.

As you step forward, another German soldier steps out from behind the half-track. You hadn't spotted him! Your last sight is the soldier pointing his gun at you. There is a flash and then darkness as you drop to the floor.

You have failed! If you wish to begin again, go to 1.

9

You are driven to a nearby Royal Air Force base, where a plane is waiting to fly you to northern France.

Before you board the plane, you are taken to a Nissen hut where an Air Force orderly has prepared the equipment for your mission. He hands over maps, a compass, false identity papers, a torch, a knife, a Webley revolver and a new rifle...

If you want to find out more about the new rifle, go to 34.

If you want to head straight to the plane, go to 14.

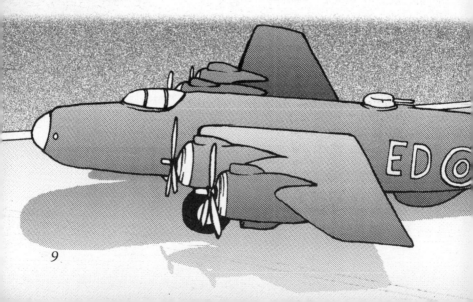

10

"I can't go anywhere," you say to the man.

He laughs. "I will help you down," he says. "Cut yourself free and I will catch you."

You do as he says and soon you are down safely on the ground. However, you are still not sure if the man is to be trusted.

If you wish to attack the man, go to 15.

If you decide to talk to him, go to 26.

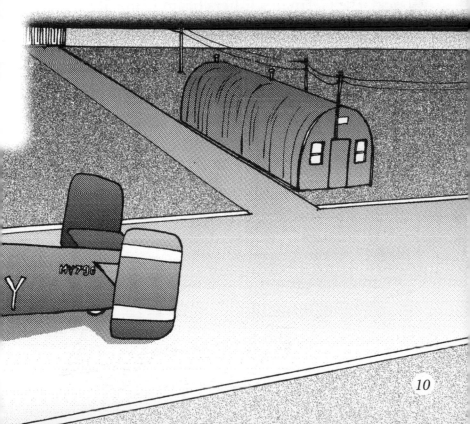

11

You sit surrounded by soldiers as the truck takes you to the German HQ.

Suddenly there is a roar of an aeroplane's engines from outside and the sound of bullets hitting the ground. The truck is being attacked! It comes to a halt and the soldiers leap out. You and the woman follow them. Above you an RAF fighter plane is coming in for a second attack! The German soldiers begin firing at it.

If you wish to take cover under the truck, go to 38.

If you wish to try and escape, go to 42.

12

You wake up, feeling groggy. Looking up, you see a German soldier standing over you.

"You are a British spy," he says. "For you the war is over... The Gestapo are waiting to interrogate you."

There is no escape. If you wish to begin the adventure again, go to 1.

13

Even though you realise that travelling in daylight is dangerous, you decide to leave immediately.

The woman gives you a bicycle and you set off for the chateau.

You haven't travelled very far, when you see a German army truck heading at speed down the road towards you.

It pulls up and a dozen soldiers leap out. There is only one place to hide – a barn at the side of the road.

If you wish to fight the soldiers, go to 21.
If you wish to hide in the barn, go to 46.

14

It is dark as the plane takes off and heads towards France.

After an hour of flying, the pilot calls you into the cockpit. "French coast ahead," he says.

Looking out, you can just see the outline of the Normandy coast. You know that this is where thousands of Allied troops will be landing in a month's time, so your mission must succeed!

Suddenly the air is lit up and the plane is rocked by a series of explosions.

"Flak!" shouts the pilot. The shells burst around you, buffeting the plane violently.

"This is bad!" says the pilot. "I'm not sure we'll get through this! Shall we turn back?"

If you wish to order the pilot to turn back, go to 48.

If you wish to continue, go to 5.

15

You thrust your hand towards your holster, but are too slow. There is a flash and a loud crack.

You feel a searing pain in your chest, then nothing. You have failed and paid the ultimate price.

Your adventure is over. If you wish to start again, go to 1.

16

Despite the woman's protests, you decide to wait until it is dark. You settle down to sleep in the barn.

Some time later you are woken by the sound of a truck. You peer out of the barn and see a group of German soldiers jumping out of the vehicle. They break into the farmhouse and bring out the woman at gunpoint. Then they head towards the barn.

If you wish to fight your way out of the barn, go to 21.

If you wish to stay hidden in the barn, go to 46.

17

As the German soldiers spray bullets at you, the Resistance members leap out of the half-track and open fire. However, to your horror, they are soon cut down by the enemy.

Latrec and the code-machine are bundled into the black car. You can only look on helplessly as the car speeds away and bullets smash into the balcony around you.

More soldiers pour into the courtyard, shooting at you.

Go to 21.

18

You crash into the trees before coming to a jarring stop as your chute is caught on a branch.

As you dangle helplessly fifteen metres above the ground, you hear twigs snap below you. Someone is coming your way.

If you wish to cut yourself free from the parachute webbing, go to 3.

If you decide to keep quiet and hope you are not seen, go to 35.

19

"When do you need an answer?" you ask.

"Good heavens!" cries the general. "We don't have a minute to lose! Thousands of Allied lives will be at risk if the Nazis break our codes! I need your decision now!"

Go to 27.

20

The Resistance fighters prepare a bomb on the way to the chateau. As you approach the German HQ, you see that there is a heavily guarded checkpoint.

If you want to stop at the checkpoint, go to 28.

If you want to drive through it, go to 45.

21

You open fire but it is a hopeless situation. There are far too many German soldiers.

You fight on heroically, before you feel a blow to your chest. You look down and see blood pouring down your body. It is the last sight you see as your eyes close and you drop to the floor.

You have failed. If you wish to begin the adventure again, go back to 1.

22

You creep as quietly as you can further into the forest. You see a fallen tree and hide behind it.

As you lie on the ground, you hear a voice calling out. "Hello, I know you are here. I saw your parachute. I have to speak to you."

If you wish to talk to the man, go to 26.
If you wish to attack him, go to 47.

23

The air beats at your body as you drop towards the ground. You have to decide how quickly you wish to open your parachute. The longer you leave it, the less chance there is that someone on the ground will spot you, but you will have less control over your landing spot.

If you wish to wait to open your chute, go to 7.

If you wish to open your chute straight away, go to 49.

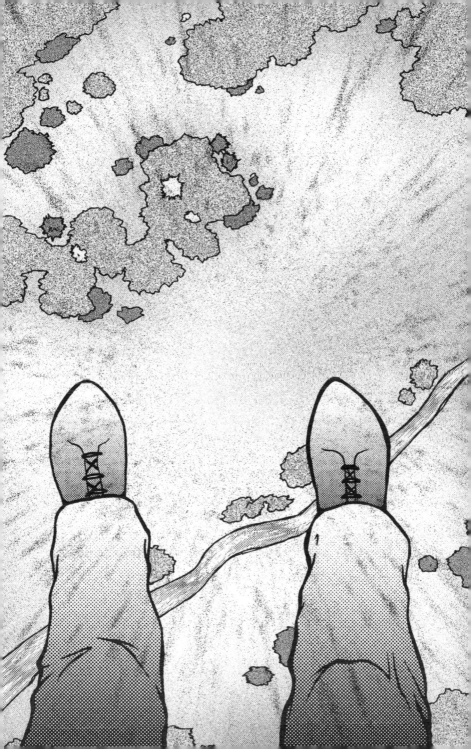

24

"Of course I know that they are here," you tell the sentry. "They have asked for my help. Let me through, or I'll see you stay on sentry duty for the next month!"

The sentry apologises and raises the barrier.

You pass through and head towards the chateau. As you drive the half-track into the courtyard, you notice that there is a black car parked near the main door. The driver is filling the car with petrol from a jerry can. There are more cans over at the far side of the courtyard near a large Panzer tank. You park the half-track and step out, just as a squad of German soldiers appear.

If you wish to attack the soldiers, go to 21.
If you wish to talk to them, go to 32.

25

You pull the trigger carefully and the Gestapo officer falls to the floor, dropping the machine. However, the Germans quickly realise where the shot has come from and return fire.

Go to 17.

26

Although you decide to talk to the man, you are still cautious. "It is a dark night to be wandering in the forest, Monsieur," you say stepping forward.

The man looks at you. "What is your name?" he asks.

"Smith," you reply.

He smiles. "I was expecting you, Smith. I am with the Resistance. You must come with me. I will take you to where Latrec is being held."

"And what is your name?" you ask.

"Jacques le Rouge," he says.

If you don't trust the man, go to 2.
If you want to go with him to Latrec, go to 6.

27

"I'm up for it! What do you want me to do?" you ask.

"I need you to get over to France, find Latrec and discover if the Nazis have got the machine. If they have, then you have to locate and destroy it. We'll make arrangements with the French Resistance to meet you and escort you to where Latrec is being held. We'll fly you in tonight. Do you have any questions?"

If you wish to ask any questions about the mission, go to 44.

If you want to get on with the mission, go to 9.

28

You stop the half-track at the checkpoint. The sentries salute.

In perfect German, you tell one of the sentries that you are here to help interrogate the prisoner.

The sentry looks suspicious and tells you that the Gestapo have already arrived.

If you want to drive through the barrier, go to 45.

If you want to talk further to the sentry, go to 24.

If you want to open fire on the sentries, go to 21.

29

You pull on the parachute's webbing and you drift away from the trees. You brace yourself for landing as the ground rushes towards you.

You land perfectly and quickly gather your parachute up. Then you hurry towards the forest to hide your chute in the undergrowth.

As you are burying the chute, you hear a twig snap. You peer into the darkness and can make out the figure of a man, ten metres away, dressed in civilian clothes and carrying a rifle.

If you wish to hide, go to 22.

If you wish to attack the man, go to 47.

If you wish to talk to him, go to 26.

30

In order to try and save your life, you tell the German commander everything about your mission. He nods and orders one of his men to radio the chateau to tell them the importance of the machine.

Then he turns to you. "I think you have outlived your usefulness."

He points his pistol at you. You see a flash of light then nothing more.

You have paid the ultimate price for revealing your mission. If you wish to start again, go to 1.

31

You and the woman make your way through the ditch and across the field, avoiding the firing from the half-track.

You arrive at the back of the farmhouse, where you are let in and introduced to four members of the Resistance.

The gunfire from the soldiers in the half-track is heavy.

"We can't stay here," you say. "The Germans will radio for help – we have to act now."

Go to 4.

32

"Where is the prisoner?" you ask.

A soldier salutes and points towards the chateau. "The Gestapo have him upstairs. I wouldn't like to be in his shoes." You thank the soldiers and head into the chateau with your rifle, leaving the Resistance members with the half-track and their bomb.

You hurry upstairs, but there is no sign of Latrec. Suddenly you hear shouting from outside and step out onto a balcony to see what is happening. In the courtyard below, you see Latrec being escorted to the black car by Gestapo officers. One of the officers is holding the code-machine!

If you raise your rifle and fire quickly, go to 41.

If you want to wait a few extra seconds to take aim, go to 37.

33

You follow the woman across the fields. The sun is rising as you arrive at a farmhouse.

The woman takes you to a barn, where there is food and drink waiting for you. While you eat, the woman tells you where Latrec is being held. "Our contacts say he has been taken to the local chateau," she says. "The Gestapo are on their way from Paris to interrogate him. You don't have much time."

If you want to head to the chateau now, go to 13.

If you decide to wait until night, go to 16.

34

"That looks like a De Lisle rifle," you say.

"That's right. Accurate up to 250 metres," replies the orderly. "And it can fire 20 rounds a minute."

He hands over the rifle and you head outside to board the plane.

Go to 14.

35

As you hang helplessly in the tree, a man appears on the path below you. He is dressed in civilian clothes and is carrying a rifle.

Your heart is in your mouth as the man stops. You start to reach for your revolver, but as you do, he looks up and sees you.

The man laughs and points his rifle at you. "Do not move, please."

If you want to try and reach your gun, go to 15.

If you decide to wait to see what the man says, go to 10.

36

"I'll only give you my name, rank and serial number," you tell the German commander.

He nods. "Very well. I think a visit to the Gestapo will change that."

The soldiers lead you to the truck and bundle you in. Already sitting in the truck is the French woman.

"Don't worry, everything will be all right," you say. But in your heart you know you are in trouble.

Go to 11.

37

You realise that you will only have time for one clear burst. You aim the rifle carefully, but do you shoot the machine or the officer?

If you decide to shoot the Gestapo officer carrying the machine, go to 25.

If you decide to shoot the machine, go to 40.

38

You dive under the truck as the plane screams overhead. You hear the whine of a bomb falling.

The last sound you hear is an explosion as the bomb hits the truck turning it into a fireball.

You have failed. If you wish to start your adventure again, go to 1.

39

You step forward and shoot above the heads of the German soldiers. You order them to surrender. They realise their position is hopeless. They lay down their guns and raise their hands.

The Resistance fighters finish off the other soldiers and join you. You explain your mission to destroy the code-machine. "We'll use the German uniforms and take their half-track," you say. "That way we'll get into the chateau."

Three volunteers disguise themselves in the German soldiers' uniforms. You put on an officer's uniform and say goodbye to the woman. You thank her for her help. Then you all set off in the half-track towards the chateau.

Go to 20.

40

You take aim and fire. The code-machine is blasted apart! Your next bullet is aimed at the jerry cans near the Panzer tank. They explode and the Panzer tank bursts into flames. Thick smoke fills the courtyard.

Go to 50.

41

You open fire, but in your haste you shoot wide and miss.

The Gestapo officers realise that they are under attack and order the soldiers to return fire.

Go to 17.

42

The German soldiers are too busy to see you reaching into the truck and grabbing your rifle. You and the woman hide in a ditch at the edge of a cornfield.

As the plane roars away, another stream of bullets hits the truck. The attack is coming from a farmhouse.

"It is the Resistance," says the woman.

The battle is intense and the Resistance inflict many casualties. However, just as it seems that victory is won, a German armoured half-track appears and begins firing at the farmhouse.

"They need help," says the woman.

If you wish to make your way to the farmhouse, go to 31.

If you decide to head into the cornfield behind the half-track, go to 4.

43

You brace yourself for your landing. The ground rushes towards you and you hit it at full force. You are bowled over and your head crashes against the hard ground. You feel a brief searing pain, then nothing more as you pass out.

Go to 12.

44

"How will I know if the French Resistance contact is genuine?" you ask. "Latrec might have been captured because he was betrayed."

"Jolly good point," says the general. "We will radio a password name to the Resistance. When your contact asks you for your name, you reply, 'Smith'."

"And what will the contact's password be?" you ask.

"The contact's codename will be 'Pierre Blanc'," replies the general. "Now, you need to get to the airfield, we don't have a minute to lose."

Go to 9.

45

You slam your foot on the accelerator and send the half-track crashing through the wooden barrier.

The German sentries open fire. Your three companions shoot back.

As you hurtle down the drive towards the chateau, a German Panzer tank appears and begins firing at you.

You try to avoid the exploding shells, but one bursts in front of you, bringing the half-track to a shuddering halt. You and the Resistance members jump out of the burning vehicle to face the enemy.

Go to 21.

46

You head for the back of the barn, but before you can hide, the soldiers burst in, guns pointing at you, shouting, "Surrender!"

You realise your situation is hopeless. You drop your weapon and raise your hands.

The German commander steps forward. "We know you parachuted here, what is your mission? Tell us and we will spare you."

If you decide to tell them about your mission, go to 30.

If you decide not to, go to 36.

47

You leap out, revolver at the ready. But before you can pull the trigger, the man sees you and disappears into the trees. You curse and follow him.

However, it is dark and the undergrowth is thick, causing you to stumble. As you pick yourself up off the ground you hear the crack of a branch to your left. You spin around, but before you can do anything, the man leaps out. The last sight you see is a swinging rifle butt. It cracks you on the side of the head and you fall to the floor, unconscious.

Go to 12.

48

"Turn back," you order the pilot. "We'll have to try another route in."

The pilot obeys and pulls on the control stick. However, as he does so, there is an enormous explosion and the wing of the plane falls apart.

"We're hit! Bail out!" screams the pilot. You struggle towards the door, but it is too late. Another shell explodes, engulfing the plane in a ball of fire.

Your adventure is over. If you wish to start again, go to 1.

49

You pull on the ripcord and your chute opens up above you. As you float down, you realise that you are heading towards a small forest. It will give you cover from any prying eyes, but the landing will be dangerous.

If you wish to try and land away from the forest, go to 29.

If you decide to land in the forest, go to 18.

50

In the chaos and confusion you rush downstairs into the courtyard. You see that Latrec has been rescued by the Resistance members. The Gestapo officers lie dead on the ground.

You leap onboard the half-track as it speeds away, smashing through the gate, just as a huge explosion rocks the chateau. You turn to see clouds of flame leaping into the air.

"The bomb we planted," explains a Resistance member. "A little present to remember us by!"

"I don't think the Nazis will forget us in a hurry," you reply.

Latrec slaps you on the back. "You are a hero!" he says.

You smile. The Allied secret plans for *Operation Overlord* will not be discovered. Your mission is a success!

Gorgon's Cave

Steve Barlow and Steve Skidmore

Illustrated by Sonia Leong

You live in the mythical world of Ancient Greece, in the time of Heracles, Theseus and Pegasus.

You are a hero, an adventurer. You have fought and won many battles against both warriors and monsters.

Now, you have been summoned by the King of the City of Thebes. Many years ago, the hero Perseus killed Medusa the gorgon. But now, Medusa's cave is once again haunted: by Medusa's sister, the gorgon Euryale; and the monster Typhon.

You make your way to the royal palace to find out what the King of Thebes has in store for you.

I HERO
DECIDE YOUR OWN DESTINY
Gorgon's Cave
Steve Barlow - Steve Skidmore